CHILDREN ON A

Text adapted by Jory Graham • Illustrations by Hildegard Lehmann

Published by BRITANNICA BOOKS, Chicago, a division of
Encyclopaedia Britannica, Inc., and distributed in association with
MEREDITH PRESS, Des Moines and New York

The True-to-Life photographs in this book are from the educational motion pictures, "Spring on the Farm," "Summer on the Farm," "Autumn on the Farm," and "Winter on the Farm," produced by Encyclopaedia Britannica Films, Inc. All the scenes in these films were photographed on a farm in Wisconsin. They show the progression of the seasons and the activities of a boy and a girl as the cycle of life on the farm turns with the seasons.

This book has been carefully manufactured for long wear. The paper is 100-pound coated stock specially created for this series. The pages are side-sewn, and are fixed into the case with sturdy end sheets. The laminated cover resists dirt and is washable.

The design of this book is by the noted husband-wife team of artists, Alex and Janet D'Amato.

The body type of this book is 20-point Weiss Italic, a type face which suggests the script of a boy's letter home.

LIBRARY OF CONGRESS CATALOG NUMBER: 62-13223
PRINTED IN THE UNITED STATES OF AMERICA

FIRST PRINTING 1962
SECOND PRINTING 1962

SPRING

Mother was sick. She needed a long rest. Daddy said, "Would you children like to live on the farm with Aunt Sue and Uncle Bill?"

The farmhouse was big. It was much bigger than our apartment in the city.

We got a kite to fly because it was spring. Boy! How that kite flew! The wind carried it way up high. While I was pulling the kite in, Joan went to the apple orchard. The trees were covered with blossoms.

I ran after Joan and climbed up an apple tree. In a fork of the tree I found a nest of baby robins.

"What did you find, Jerry?" called Joan.

I told her. She wanted to see the baby robins, too, but she was afraid to climb the tree. I let the robins alone. I didn't want to hurt them.

We found many new things. We found the robin's nest, and we found a baby bunny hiding in the grass. I tried to pet it, but it hopped away.

Beyond the orchard was a field where Uncle Bill kept his sheep. The sheep had lambs. The lambs looked at us as we stood by the fence.

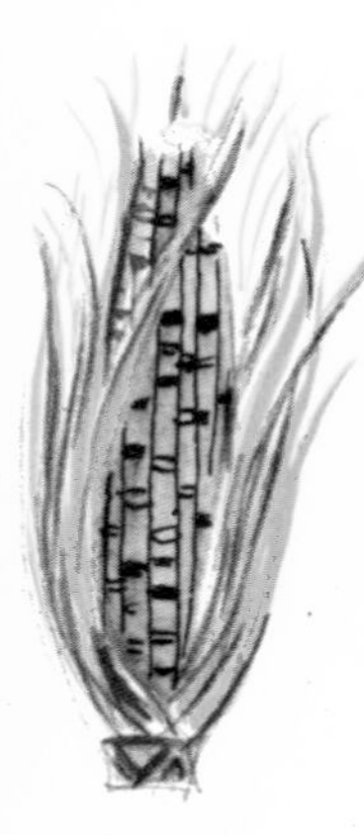

One morning Uncle Bill said, "This is the day we plant the corn." When we got to the edge of the field, Uncle Bill picked up a handful of earth. It smelled fresh and moist.

I helped Uncle Bill pour seed into the corn planter, then he drove it back and forth across the field. It planted corn in straight rows.

While I was helping Uncle Bill, Joan helped Aunt Sue plant the garden behind the house. They planted beans, lettuce, radishes, beets, and other things. Aunt Sue dug a trench with a hoe, and Joan put the seeds in the trench. In the summer we would eat the vegetables, Aunt Sue said.

Baby chicks were hatching in the incubator. We watched them break their shells open and come out. They were wet at first, but then they dried and became fluffy. Baby chicks are soft.

Once, in a storm, a tree fell across the creek. We would run across the old log to the pasture where the cows were. We drove the cows home for milking.

SUMMER

In summer, when it got hot, the cows looked for shade under the trees. Joan and I put on farm hats. It was very quiet down at the pond where we fished. One day we caught six fish and ate them for supper!

Early in July I helped Uncle Bill cut the hay. He let me drive the big tractor to pull the hay to the barn. He said he would feed the hay to the cows and sheep next winter.

The corn that Uncle Bill had planted grew tall under the hot summer sun. Tassels grew on the tops of the stalks. Young ears of corn grew along the sides of the stalks.

When corn gets this high, you can hide in it. You can get lost in a cornfield. Joan and I liked to play hide and seek in the cornfield.

Joan got a surprise while she was picking flowers.
She saw a spider spinning a web to catch flies.

We went to pick blackberries. They tasted so good we ate more than we put in the bucket.

We picked the tomatoes when they were ripe.
Tomatoes turn a beautiful red as they get ripe.

Watermelons stay green on the outside even when they're ripe. Uncle Bill pointed to a watermelon that he said was ready to eat. He let us pick it. We carried it from the field all the way to the house. Boy! Watermelons are heavy!

When you bite into a watermelon,
the sweet juice gets all over you.
The juice ran down to my
elbow. I love watermelon!

AUTUMN

The trees turn bright colors in the fall. The beech trees turn yellow. Maples turn red. The oaks turn orange and brown.

The apple trees that were covered with blossoms in the spring were covered with apples in the fall. The apples had such a good apple smell.

Uncle Bill put a ladder into a tree. He let me climb way up the ladder. I picked the best apple from the top of the tree and gave it to Joan.

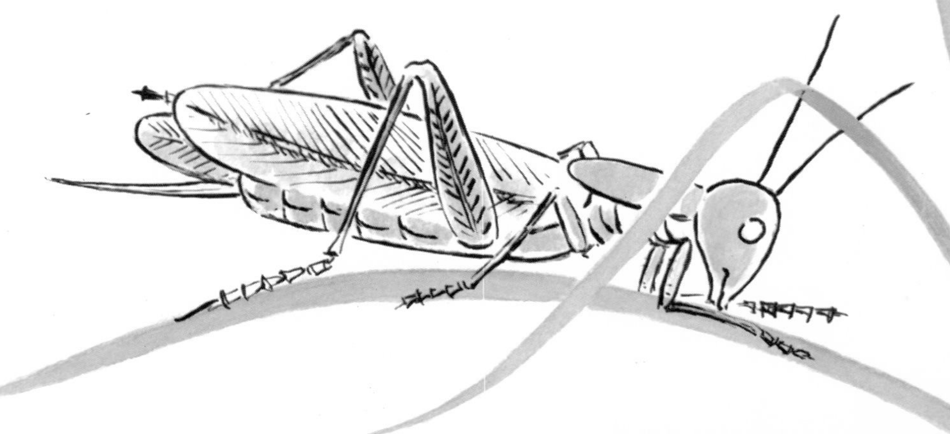

Apples have a kind of wax on the outside. When you rub them, they shine. We rubbed some of the apples against our sleeves to see them shine. We put all the apples we picked in baskets. We thought about all the good things apples can be — apple pie, apple sauce, taffy apples. Every now and then we ate an apple.

Joan and I carried a basket of apples back to the house. We had to rest along the way. While we rested we looked at the yellow goldenrod.

Other fruits were ripe, too. There were big bunches of purple grapes called Concord grapes. They were soft and juicy, and they tasted warm from the sun.

We picked the grapes and took them into the house. Aunt Sue was busy making the grapes into jelly.

At last the corn was ripe. Uncle Bill drove a corn picker through the field. It stripped off the husks and dropped the ears of corn into a wagon.

When the corn stalks were tied into shocks, they looked like tepees. And on the ground were pumpkins! They had been growing along the ground under the corn all summer.

After the frosts came, nuts began to fall. I pointed out to Joan where the nut trees were. We took pails along to gather the nuts.

We went into the woods. A lot of leaves had fallen. We scuffled through them and found walnuts. They have a round outside shell and a hard inside shell. When you pinch off the outside shell, you get walnut stain on your fingers. The walnut stain stays a long time.

Squirrels were out gathering nuts, too. A little brown chipmunk with a nut in his mouth sat up and watched us. There were branches covered with bright red leaves. Joan picked a big bunch of them for Aunt Sue.

The turkeys were getting big and plump. Turkeys are funny birds. They let you feed them corn, but you can't pet them. They really do say, "Gobble! Gobble!"

WINTER

One night in winter it began to snow. The next morning the farm was white. The whole world was so quiet we thought we should tiptoe.

Uncle Bill gave us a sled and an axe. He said we could find our own Christmas tree.

Christmas! Our parents were coming and then we would all go home together. I said, "Let's find the prettiest tree in the woods!"

We looked and looked and found just the right one. Everybody was pleased with the tree. We had the best Christmas ever!